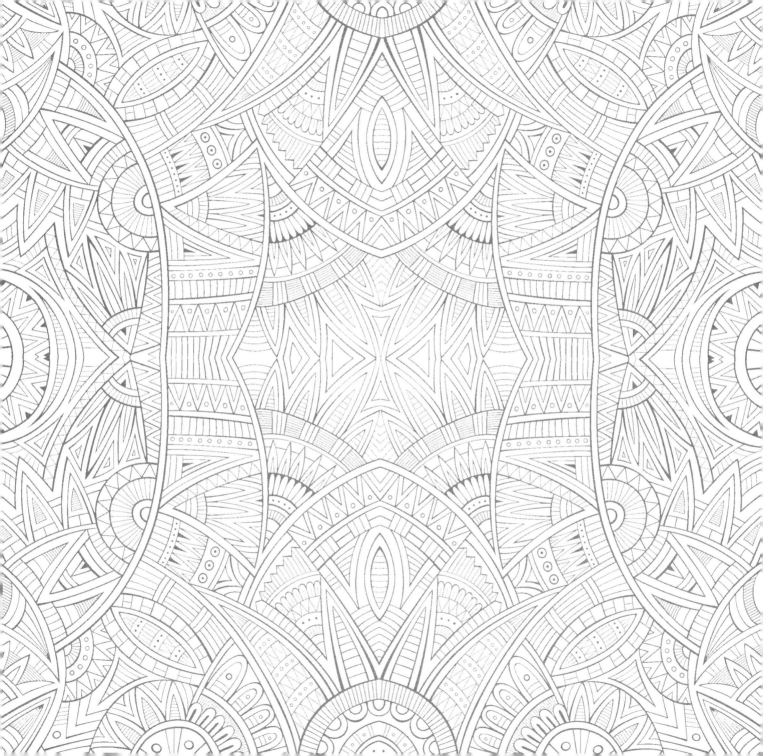

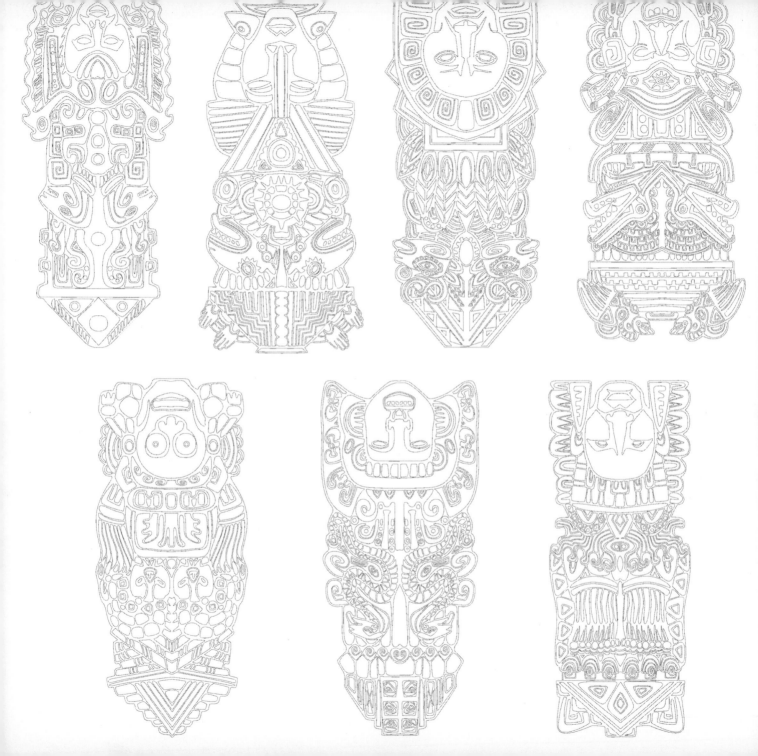

CREDITS
Cover : © Balabolka/Shutterstock
Interior : p. 1, 12, 20, 24 : © LizaLutik/Shutterstock ; p. 2, 11, 14, 30, 41, 48, 69 : © Balabolka/Shutterstock ; p. 2, 15, 36 : © Kristina Birukova/Shutterstock ; p. 3, 12, 13, 34, 36, 37, 38, 39, 44, 47, 57, 59, 62, 66, 68 : © Julia Snegireva/Shutterstock ; p. 4, 34 : © fbf/Shutterstock ; p. 5, 21, 51, 55, 63 : © Andrei Verner/Shutterstock ; p. 6, 7, 10, 16, 17, 19, 27, 28, 48, 60 : © Liukas/Shutterstock; p. 8, 22, 33, 43, 50, 65, 70 : © Rorius/Shutterstock; p. 9 : © Uniyok/Shutterstock; p. 18, 45 : © De-V/Shutterstock ; p. 23, 58 : © Irmairma/Shutterstock ; p. 25 : © mountain beetie/Shutterstock ; p. 29, 54, 64 : © Lola Tsvetaeva/Shutterstock ; p. 31, 56 : © Malikamir/Shutterstock ; p. 32, 71 : © IrinaKrivoruchko/Shutterstock ; p. 40 : © Aqua5/Shutterstock ; p. 42 : © Maria Erypalova/Shutterstock ; p. 46, 67 : © Kate Vogel/Shutterstock; p. 49, 72 : ©Transia design/Shutterstock ; p. 52 : © Karakotsya/Shutterstock ; p. 53 : © Gorbash Varvara/Shutterstock

An Hachette UK Company
www.hachette.co.uk

First published in France in 2015 by Dessain et Tolra

This edition published in Great Britain in 2015 by Hamlyn,
a division of Octopus Publishing Group Ltd
Carmelite House, 50 Victoria Embankment, London EC4Y 0DZ
www.octopusbooks.co.uk

ISBN 978-0-600-63294-8

A CIP catalogue record for this book is available from the
British Library.

Printed and bound in Italy
10 9 8 7 6 5 4 3 2 1

Publishing directors: Isabelle Jeuge-Maynart, Ghislaine Stora
Editorial direction: Stéphanie Auvergnat, Florence Pierron-Boursot
Editor: Barbara Janssens
Cover: Fanny Tallégas, Abigail Read
Layout: Fanny Tallégas
Senior production manager: Katherine Hockley